Into the Woods for a Basket of Soup

A **Fox in Pepper Green Socks** Story

First Edition in a Series

Based on the Poem, "A Basket of Soup" by Thomas Richard Smith

Co-Author Kimberly Smith Andreadis

Illustrated by Rebekah Keener

November, 2020

North Bethesda, Maryland

Published in the United States of America

ISBN 978-1-7360224 -0-5 (eBook)
ISBN 978-1-7360224 -1-2 (print/paperback)

First Edition, November 2020

A Letter to the Parents

The Story: A young boy is sitting on his porch at dusk. He is wondering what to do next.
He is bored; there are no children around to play with. He feels sad and he is wishing
he had some company. He begins to listen to the sounds around him in the night.
The trees are rustling. Then he notices some movement in the woods in front of him.
He is very curious.

What are the animals up to? He observes an interesting sight; a group of animals getting
together for a meal. In the end, the boy is very curious about the fox. There is something
very different about the fox.

Into the Woods for a Basket of Soup is a Read and Learn Club publication. The illustrations
are designed to be provocative. The reader is provided with opportunities to learn and
to teach, a new word, an idea or a concept.

At the back of the book, find information about the animals in this book and how they
live. You will also find some questions for discussion.

Look for more read and learn books and stories about the fox in pepper green socks at
www.foxinpeppergreensocks.com

I was sitting there grieving

Hardly believing

All the things that were

Whispering that night

I was sullen with sorrow

Fearing tomorrow

Until I saw

Such a beautiful sight

An ancient white owl

Was chasing a fowl

When along came a fox

In pepper green socks

And a Mongoose

Was humming a tune

They circled around

A little gray hound

While a lizard

Was kissing the moon

A fluffy brown bear

Was scratching his hair

While away from the wood

A possum still stood

So reluctant at joining the group

Until a wisp of the wind

Invited him in

And they all had

A basket of soup

They were waggish and smiling

Simply beguiling

What a night

Has this night ever been?

And I am thinking of staying

Hopefully praying

That I will meet

All these creatures again

As for the fox

In pepper green socks

I won't rest until

I learn more

This fox is quite cunning

His socks, simply stunning

There is a mystery

Here to Explore

A Basket of Soup Teaching Guide

Topics for Discussion with Your Child

1. What kind of animals do you find in this story?

2. How many animals are in this story?

3. One of the animals was wearing an item of clothing;
   which one and what were they wearing?

4. Were the animals sharing?

5. What were they sharing?

6. How are the animals sharing?

7. Are they enjoying each other's company?

8. Why was the little boy surprised?

9. Do you think he wants to join them and have some soup too?

10. What kind of soup do you think they are having?

11. What kind of soup do you like?

12. What kinds of sounds "whisper" in the night?

Fun Facts about the Animals

You can more about these animals on the Internet or at your local library.

 The **red fox** has a reputation for being clever. Groups of fox are called a skulk or a leash. Foxes have whiskers on their face and legs which help them to move around quickly and easily. A male fox is called a dog and a female is called a vixen. Their children are called "kids." Foxes have excellent hearing. They can hear a watch ticking 40 yards away.

 The **snowy white owl** has a reputation for being wise and watchful. It is usually found in North American arctic regions. But they do fly as far south as Georgia in the United States. The female is larger than the male. Males are solid white, while females have some gray feathers. Owls are nocturnal

 The **possum** is the size of a cat and is found in Australia. A possum is different from an opossum. Opossums are found in North America. The possum and the opossum have distinctive pink noses. They both have very sharp teeth. They are diggers and will dig a place underground to live. They are shy animals and like to avoid people and other animals.

 The **mongoose** lives in Africa and Asia, the Caribbean and in the Hawaiian Islands. Many like to live in the tree tops and some are excellent swimmers. They sleep at night, like people. They are not good diggers so they live in burrows that were dug by other animals. They have a keen sense of smell, sight and hearing. They can run up to 20 miles per hour and they giggle like humans.

Fun Facts about the Animals

You can more about these animals on the Internet or at your local library.

 The **"fowl"** is a kind of bird. In this story, the foul is a pheasant. Pheasants come in several colors. They fly short distances. A pheasant can fly straight up and make a whirling sound at the same time. They can cruise up to 37 miles per hour. Although they are good at flying, they prefer to run, Pheasants live in the woods. They hang around in groups, called flocks.

 The **brown grizzly bear** can grow to be very tall, up to nine feet! They have huge paws and long front claws. They are very good at digging. They sleep all winter long, up to six months, without eating. This is called hibernation. They like to eat vegetables, apples, berries and nuts and especially honey! They live in the forests and mountains of North America, Europe and Asia.

 **Lizards** are a kind of reptile. There are many kinds of lizards. They have walked the earth for over 200 million years and live all over the world. One kind, the chameleons can change colors, so they can hide. They can also smell with their tongues. Most lizards lie on the ground. But some live in the water, in trees and under the ground in burrows.

 The **hound dog** is a social pack animal. When the hound dog lives with a family, the family becomes their pack. They get along with other kinds of animals like horses, cows and sheep. Dogs can see much better than humans at night. They are considered to be "man's best friend". A blood hound can track another animal or even a person based on their scent. They have a great sense of smell.

About the Author

Thomas Richard Smith

Thomas Richard Smith spent his lifetime writing. He was born in 1926, in New York City the son of British and French Canadian immigrants. As a young boy he lived and attended school in a racially diverse suburb of New York City, among other immigrant families.

Later his family moved from New York City to Bridgeport, Connecticut. He left home at age 17 to join the United States Navy during WWII. He bravely participated in the Second Wave at Omaha Beach, Normandy, and the liberation of France.

After the war, he returned home to Connecticut. He earned a BA degree in Sociology at the University of Bridgeport in the first graduating class of 1947, under the GI Bill. Later he attended graduate classes in journalism at Brown and Columbia University. He met his wife, Beverly Jane Forbush while working at General Electric Corporation. They had nine children together. During their lifetime they lived primarily in the New England states. He moved to Brooksville, Florida in 2019 and passed away at age 94 in February, 2020 during the world wide corona virus pandemic.

He spent his career in business as a product inventor and marketing manager, yet he never stopped writing poetry, short stories and limericks. He penned his last poem just two weeks prior to passing.

His participation in the war impacted his view of the world and motivated him to search for beauty, love and harmony through the written word. He has authored over 5000 poems, stories and articles. He believed that the best way to teach children the English language was by teaching them to read and learn how to write rhymes. In the early years, his children became his audience as he wrote and read his stories and poems and sang his songs to them endlessly. Prior to his passing he requested that his oldest daughter, Kimberly Smith Andreadis assemble and publish some of his writings, most of which had never been published before.

About the Co-Author

Kimberly Smith Andreadis

Kimberly Smith Andreadis is the oldest daughter of Thomas Richard Smith. She lives in the Washington DC Metro area with her husband, Dr. Themistoklis Andreadis, a research physicist. She has appeared in many theatrical productions in New England summer stock as a child and young adult. She later attended the prestigious Actor's Mobile Theater in New York City with drama coach, Brett Warren.

Before continuing her education, she took a year off to manage a guest ranch in Wyoming where her love for nature and animals and her equestrian skills thrived. Life on a ranch 30 miles from the nearest neighbor meant daily involvement with a variety of animals, both domestic and wild.

During her father's lifetime, she organized writer's workshops, where local poets and writers met to share their craft. She later attended the University of Maryland, Global Campus, where she met her husband. After a 20 year career in Sales and Marketing she is now focused on writing children's books and publishing her father's poetry and short stories. She has founded the Read and Learn Club dedicated to her daughters, Tanya and Ana and her grandchildren, Khalea and Khari. **www.foxinpeppergreensocks.com**

About the Illustrator
Rebekah Keener

Rebekah Keener feels strongly that all animals deserve to have their personalities painted, preferably in acrylic with lots of thin layers to build up pigments. She also enjoys digital illustration because she doesn't have to worry about cats tracking paint across her work. She has been painting on a commission basis since 1991. This is her first book illustration project. She lives in Northern Virginia with her husband, two sons, and several other creatures. You can find her on Facebook at **RJK@PortraitsofYourPets.com**_

CPSIA information can be obtained
at www.ICGtesting.com
Printed in the USA
BVHW091805061120
592651BV00001B/6